LEARN TOGETHER

MATHSKILLS PRACTICE 2

Games, puzzles and investigations for maths practice

Roger Hepworth

A Piccolo Original
Piccolo Books

DIGITAL DOTS

Use your tables to work out the answers then join up the dots in numerical order to reveal the mystery picture.

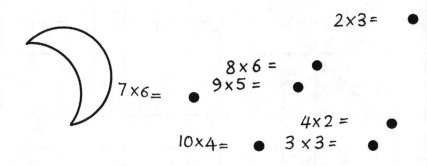

$2 \times 3 =$ •

$8 \times 6 =$ •
$9 \times 5 =$ •

$7 \times 6 =$ •

$4 \times 2 =$ •
$10 \times 4 =$ • $3 \times 3 =$ •

$3 \times 4 =$ •

$5 \times 2 =$ •

$4 \times 8 =$ • $9 \times 4 =$ •

$7 \times 2 =$ •

$7 \times 4 =$ •
$6 \times 5 =$ • $5 \times 5 =$ •
$5 \times 4 =$ •
$6 \times 3 =$ • $5 \times 3 =$ •
$6 \times 4 =$ •

$3 \times 7 =$ •

$4 \times 4 =$ •

A ½ IS A ½ IS A ½

Colour one half of each large square. Use as many different ways as you can think of. Some lines have already been drawn to help you and the first one has been done for you.

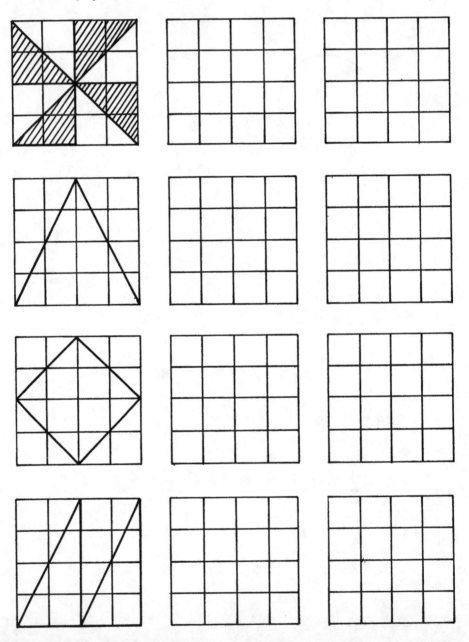

PATTERNS WITH TEN

Use a ruler to join the numbers which add up to ten. Colour in the patterns you make. The first diagram has been started for you.

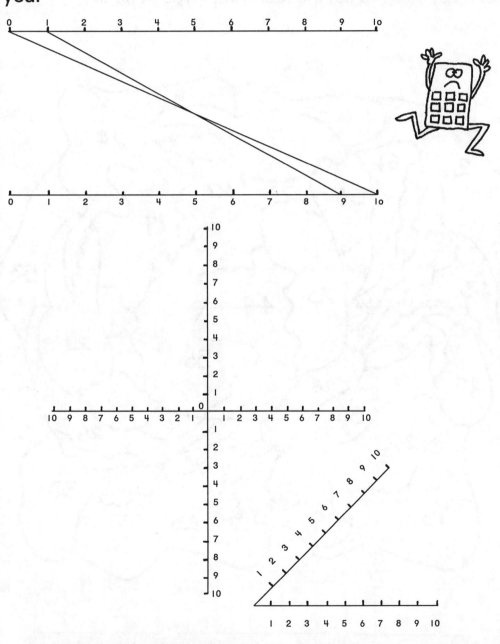

WHAT IS IT?

Use your 7× table to reveal the mystery picture. Carefully colour in every area which has a number that will divide exactly by 7. Write out the table first if you need to.

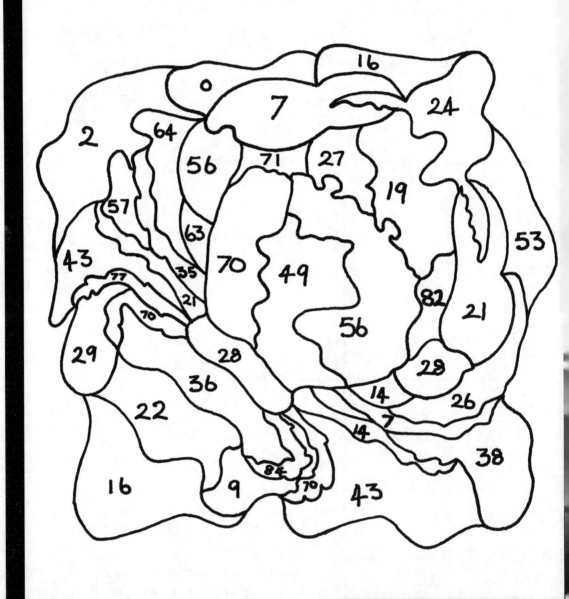

BOXED IN

Can you fill in the missing numbers in these puzzles?

In each puzzle, add the pairs of numbers from left to right and then top to bottom, writing the answer beside or below.

When these new numbers are added together, they must equal the number in the 'corner' box. The first one has been filled in for you, as an example.

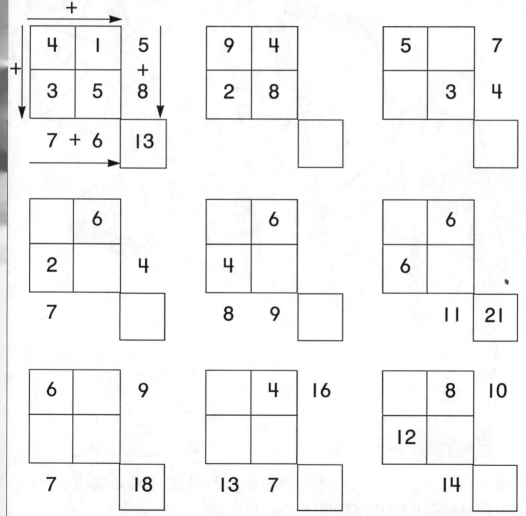

TWENTY UP

Stick this net onto card and then cut it out. Score all the lines, then bend along these lines and glue the net together using the tabs provided.

The solid shape you have made is called an Icosahedron and you can use it to astonish your friends!

Here is a chart of the pairs of numbers printed opposite each other on the Icosahedron. Add up these pairs of numbers.

1 ⟶ 19	1+19=
2 ⟶ 18	2+18=
3 ⟶ 17	3+17=
4 ⟶ 16	4+16=
5 ⟶ 15	5+15=
6 ⟶ 14	6+14=
7 ⟶ 13	7+13=
8 ⟶ 12	8+12=
9 ⟶ 11	9+11=
10 ⟶ 10	10+10=

What do you notice? _____

If you can memorise these pairs of numbers, you'll be able to amaze your friends by telling them the number on the hidden face of the Icosahedron!

How quickly can you give each of these numbers a partner so that each pair makes 20?

14	11	19	16	12	18	15	10	13	17

3	10	9	6	1	8	2	7	5	6

SQUARE DANCE

Can you see that in Set A and Set B below, the same three numbers are repeated in each line? They are all connected and once you know one, you should be able to work out the others without calculating them.

Set A

$9+2=11$
$2+9=11$
$11-2=9$
$11-9=2$

Set B

$8+5=13$
$5+8=13$
$13-5=8$
$13-8=5$

40	−	9	→	31
−				+
31				9
↓				↓
9	+	31	→	40

8	+	24	→	32

51	−	18	→	33

63	−	8	→	55
8				63

				23
				+
				17
				↓
				40

				13
				+
				15
				↓
				28

NETS

This is a plan (or net) of a cube when it is laid out.

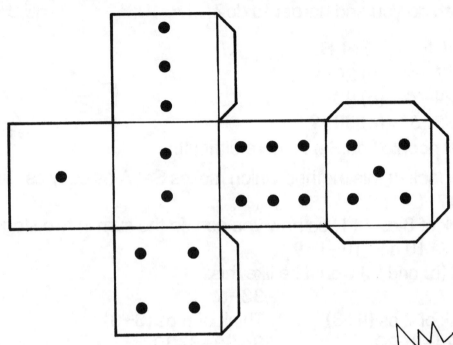

Use a ruler to copy the net accurately on thin card. Cut it out and score the lines with a sharp point before you fold them. Use the tabs to stick the sides together.

The net on this page is only one of several different nets that will fold into this particular solid. How many others can you find? You will find scissors, glue and squared paper helpful.

TAKE IT AWAY

Try these two sets of calculations in your head.
Which do you find harder to do?

Set A	Set B
(a) 17−8	(a) 20−4
(b) 24−7	(b) 40−3
(c) 33−6	(c) 30−9

Most people find Set A more difficult.

Now look at this method which makes Set A as easy as Set B.

(a) 17−8

Think of 8 as 7+1, so now you can do the sum in two stages:

17−7=10 and 10−1=9

And (b) and (c) would be like this:

24−7	33−6
Think of 7 as (4+3)	Think of 6 as (3+3)
So 24−4=20	So 33−3=30
20−3=17	30−3=27

> Did you spot that you split the number to be taken away into two numbers? One of these is the same as the units digit of the number you are taking away from.

Now try these and see if you find them easier.

23−8=	29−6=
45−6=	19−7=
35−8=	33−9=
34−7=	24−8=
22−5=	41−5=
36−9=	58−9=
13−9=	17−6=
53−8=	37−8=
43−6=	46−5=
62−7=	52−7=

ALL FOR NOUGHT

Find the difference between the pairs of numbers at the corners of the biggest square. Write the answers at the mid-point of each side and mark it out with a dot. Use a ruler to join the dots to make a smaller square.

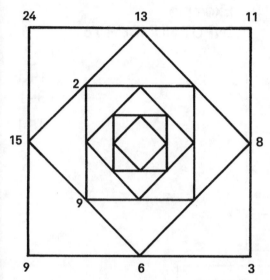

On the first square, some have already been done for you.

Choose 2 colours and colour the squares alternately.

Now do this one by yourself.

Draw some more squares and experiment with different starting numbers.

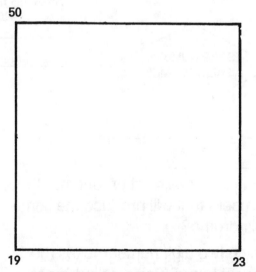

NUMBER PALINDROME

In mathematics a palindrome is a number which reads the same in both directions, e.g. 66, 121, 23632. If you follow the instructions in this flow chart carefully, you will discover a method for producing such numbers. Use a calculator to experiment with large numbers.

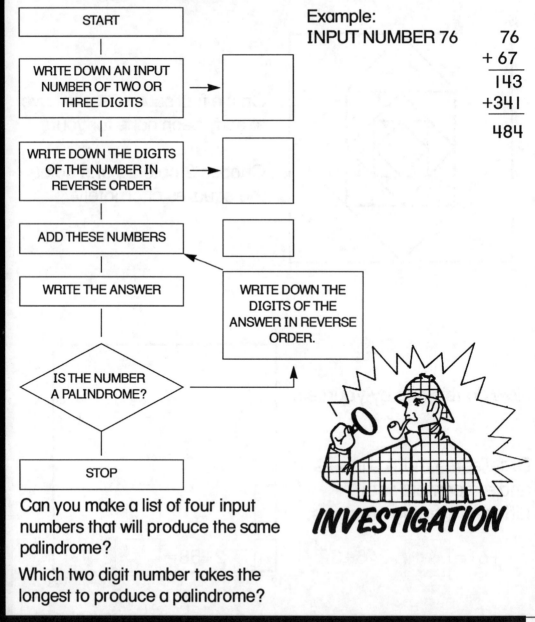

Example:
INPUT NUMBER 76

$$\begin{array}{r} 76 \\ +\ 67 \\ \hline 143 \\ +341 \\ \hline 484 \end{array}$$

START

WRITE DOWN AN INPUT NUMBER OF TWO OR THREE DIGITS

WRITE DOWN THE DIGITS OF THE NUMBER IN REVERSE ORDER

ADD THESE NUMBERS

WRITE THE ANSWER

WRITE DOWN THE DIGITS OF THE ANSWER IN REVERSE ORDER.

IS THE NUMBER A PALINDROME?

STOP

Can you make a list of four input numbers that will produce the same palindrome?

Which two digit number takes the longest to produce a palindrome?

INVESTIGATION

TURNAROUND

Try these pairs of calculations either in your head
or with a calculator.

4+5= ☐   18+2= ☐   16+7= ☐

5+4= ☐   2+18= ☐   7+16= ☐

9+16= ☐   21+12= ☐   14+18= ☐

16+9= ☐   12+21= ☐   18+14= ☐

In each pair circle the number you would start with to add:

5+43   12+2   24+3   6+70

16+12   1+20   7+10   2+34

Try turning these ones round in your head before working
out the answer:

e.g. 2+29 becomes 29+2 which =31

5+43= ☐   8+31= ☐   3+96= ☐

7+22= ☐   4+52= ☐   2+77= ☐

3+68= ☐   6+23= ☐   9+80= ☐

4+61= ☐   5+32= ☐   2+58= ☐

RICKY ROBOT

Ricky has been drawn by plotting his co-ordinates. Some examples are shown on the drawing to help you, e.g. (1,8), (1,5), (3,8), etc.

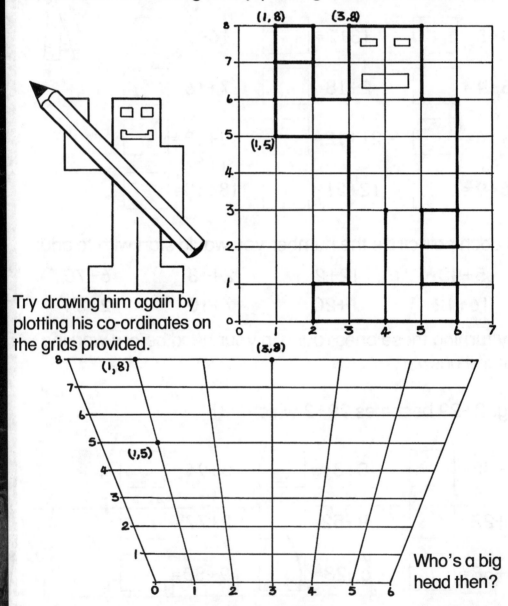

Try drawing him again by plotting his co-ordinates on the grids provided.

Who's a big head then?

Remember that co-ordinates are plotted by reading horizontally (across) first, then vertically (up and down). Try using some squared paper and doubling the numbers of each co-ordinate.

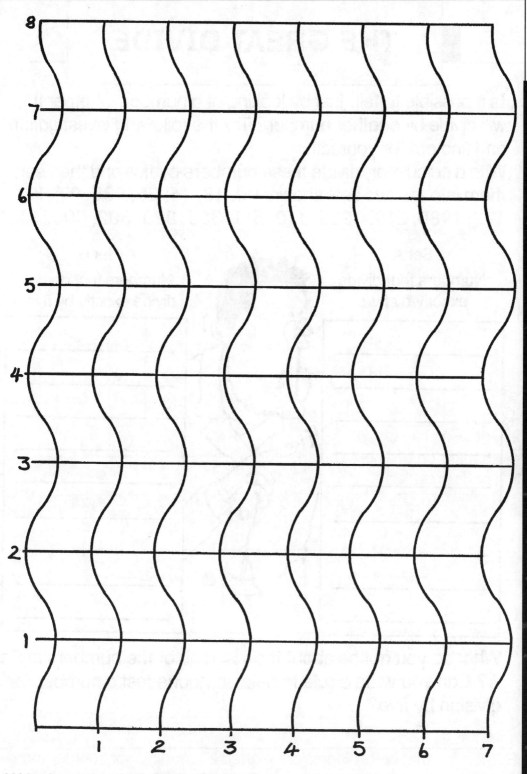

Write how you think Ricky feels now _____

THE GREAT DIVIDE

Is it possible to tell, just by looking at a number, whether it will divide by another number? Try the following investigation and find out for yourself.

With a calculator, divide these numbers by five and then sort them into the two sets shown: 40, 18, 16, 25, 935, 97, 44, 173, 1980, 219, 1235, 110, 511, 365, 820, 802, 400, 1321.

Set A

Numbers that divide exactly by five.

Set B

Numbers that do not divide exactly by five.

What do you notice about the last digit of the numbers in Set A? Can you write a rule to help someone test a number for division by five?

Now try dividing these numbers by three, then sort them into two sets as before: 12, 20, 44, 65, 93, 53, 105, 231, 540, 306, 117, 79, 118.

Set A
Numbers that divide exactly by three.

Set B
Numbers that do not divide exactly by three.

Next add up the digits of each number in Set A and divide by three again, e.g. 231 → 2+3+1=6   6÷3=2.

Now do the same with the numbers in Set B. What do you notice about these two sets of answers?

Can you write a rule to show how to test if a number will divide by three?

How about division by four?

Look at these two sets of numbers.
Set A: Numbers that divide exactly by 4: 16, 20, 424, 536, 360, 172.
Set B: Numbers that do not divide exactly by 4: 17, 23, 345, 574, 233, 191.

Try dividing just the tens and units digits of each number by four: e.g. 1128 → 28÷4=7. What do you notice about the answers?

Can you explain to a partner how to check if a number will divide exactly by four?

TENS

Here is the ten times table. Learn it by heart then write the answers of the sums in the boxes.

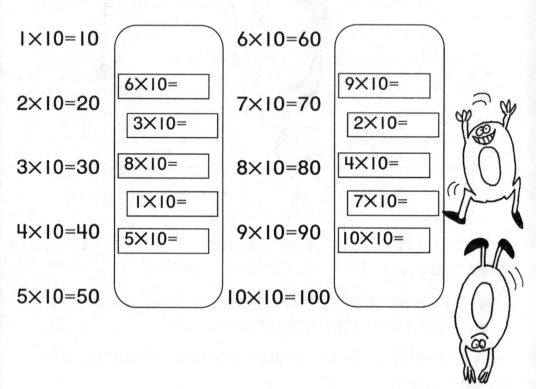

$1 \times 10 = 10$

$6 \times 10 =$

$3 \times 10 =$

$2 \times 10 = 20$

$3 \times 10 = 30$

$8 \times 10 =$

$1 \times 10 =$

$4 \times 10 = 40$

$5 \times 10 =$

$5 \times 10 = 50$

$6 \times 10 = 60$

$7 \times 10 = 70$

$8 \times 10 = 80$

$9 \times 10 = 90$

$10 \times 10 = 100$

$9 \times 10 =$

$2 \times 10 =$

$4 \times 10 =$

$7 \times 10 =$

$10 \times 10 =$

See if you can draw an arrow from each number in Set A to a number in Set B which is ten times bigger.

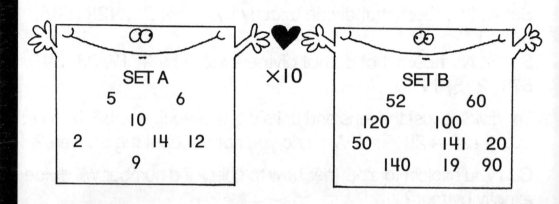

SET A

5   6
10
2   14 12
9

×10

SET B

52   60
120 100
50   141 20
140 19 90

Using the numbers from Set B, fill in this chart:

Hundreds	Tens	Units	
		2	×10
	☐	☐	
		5	×10
	☐	☐	
		6	×10
	☐	☐	
		9	×10
	☐	☐	
	1	0	×10
☐	☐	☐	
	1	2	×10
☐	☐	☐	
	1	4	×10
☐	☐	☐	

Did you spot that when a number is multiplied by 10, the digits move one column to the left?

NUMBER CROSS

Can you fit the numbers into the square?

CLUES

Across	Down
1. 28	15367
2. 49638	24
3. 51	8902
4. 5286	481
5. 733	5734
6. 905	99
7. 419	600

This one is rather more difficult.

CLUES

5261	41287
5348	48217
5624	203
5012	205
94	2473
96	91
97	4326
375	92
42187	54841

DIGITAL WALLS

Can you complete the digital wall and find which number belongs in the top brick?

4		11		
3	1	7	4	5

	9	12			
9	5	1	8	4	3	2

Can you find a quicker way of getting the answers than having to add up each pair of bricks in turn?

For Example:

6+3+3+2
6+3	3+2
6	3	2

INVESTIGATION

CLUE
Try with a small wall first and write the sums rather than the answers in each brick.

23

ADD A TEN

How many of the following can you do in 1 minute.

10+10=	10+20=	10+30=
20+10=	20+20=	20+30=
30+10=	30+20=	30+30=
40+10=	40+20=	40+30=
50+10=	50+20=	50+30=
60+10=	60+20=	60+30=
70+10=	70+20=	70+30=
80+10=	80+20=	
90+10=		

Ask someone to check your answers with a calculator.

As you can see, only the figure in the tens column changes in each calculation.

Use this hint to help you complete the following patterns quickly.

16+10=	23+10=	47+10=
16+20=	23+20=	47+20=
16+30=	23+30=	47+30=
16+40=	23+40=	47+40=
16+50=	23+50=	47+50=

Use the same hint for higher numbers.
Try doing these examples in your head while a friend does them using a calculator. You should finish first!

122+10=	156+20=	1243+20=
118+30=	131+40=	1360+31=
120+19=	143+20=	1429+70=
170+18=	164+30=	1536+30=

What about taking away whole sets of 10?

e.g. 31−10=21   53−20=33

Try these:

145−10=	298−40=	1273−60=
148−30=	281−50=	1339−20=
167−50=	241−40=	1495−90=
180−40=	239−10=	1552−30=
119−50=	246−30=	1688−70=

1...2...3... er...

HIDDEN WORDS

You will need a calculator for this activity. Complete the calculation for each clue, then turn the calculator upside-down to read the answer as a word.

Clues across

1. Stare hard ★ 47076×8
5. Short hello ★ √196
6. Surprised exclamation ★ 2000+2506
7. Ask for food or money ★ 1000−362
9. Garden tool ★ 912÷3
10. Name of boy or girl ★ 28867×11
11. Window ledge ★ 80²+1315
16. Musical instrument ★ 154×20
17. Pom poms ★ (220007+4110)×24
18. Slippery fish ★ (700−63)×9

Clues down

1. Holy book ★ 200²−2182
2. Girlish laughter ★ 2400²−380081
3. A chicken comes from this ★ 331×3
4. Footwear ★ 203×3×5+50000
8. Part of a shoe ★ 193×38
9. . . . and she ★ 100−66
10. A chunk of wood ★ 200+500−93
12. Not well ★ 1000−229
13. Misplace ★ √90000×10+507
14. Another word for earth ★ 1421×5
15. Another word for pig ★ 1000÷2+104

CONCENTRIC SHAPES

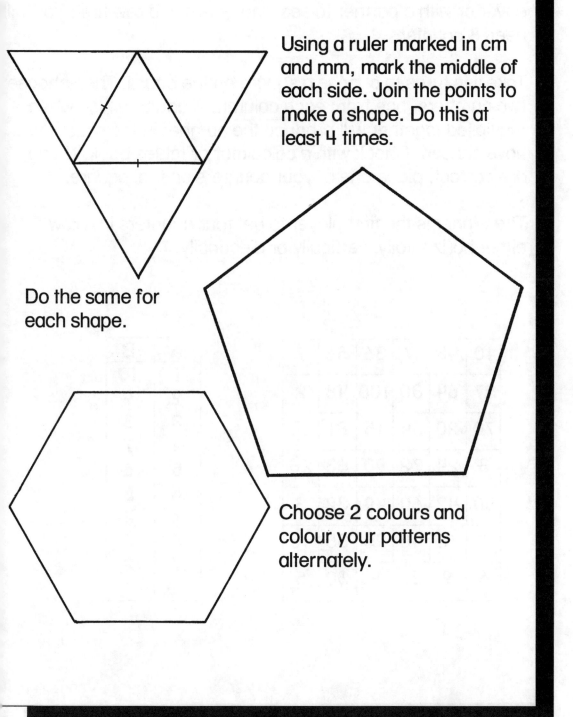

Using a ruler marked in cm and mm, mark the middle of each side. Join the points to make a shape. Do this at least 4 times.

Do the same for each shape.

Choose 2 colours and colour your patterns alternately.

FOUR IN A ROW

You can play this alone to see how many squares you can cover or with a partner to see who gets 4 in a row first. You will need 8 counters.

Take it in turns to choose a square on the board. Then choose two numbers, one from each column, A and B, which when multiplied together will produce the number in the square you have chosen. Check with a calculator or tables book. If you are correct, place one of your counters on that square.

The winner is the first player to get four counters in a row, either horizontally, vertically or diagonally.

10	45	16	36	56	7
27	64	80	100	48	2
70	20	54	15	81	14
8	24	72	90	63	28
50	42	60	49	32	3
1	12	40	25	35	18
6	9	21	4	30	5

A	B
1	10
2	9
3	8
4	7
5	6
6	5
7	4
8	3
9	2
10	1

CHECK-UP TIME

How many of these can you do in your head in 10 minutes?

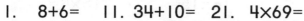

1. 8+6=	11. 34+10=	21. 4×69=
2. 9+4=	12. 70+20=	22. 5×29=
3. 9+6=	13. 45−10=	23. 3+25=
4. 19+4=	14. 82−50=	24. 6+17=
5. 26+6=	15. 53−30=	25. 46+28=
6. 38+7=	16. 79+60=	26. 36+18=
7. 24−9=	17. 9×10=	27. 75+27=
8. 46−7=	18. 8×10=	28. 62−47=
9. 23−5=	19. 11×10=	29. 55−47=
10. 16+10=	20. 3×49=	30. 35−28=

AN ASSORTMENT

Here are some sums with a difference. You will really have to put on your thinking cap.

1. Fill in the missing digit to work out which answer is correct.
   256
   + |_5   **a.** 364   **b.** 461   **c.** 351   **d.** 361

2. Using the information given in the first sum, can you fill in the missing answers without working out the whole sum each time?

   27×24=648   27×12=   15×16=240   15×8=

   24×27=   27×6=   16×15=   15×4=

   648÷27=   648÷12=   240÷16=   240÷8=

   648÷24=   648÷6=   240÷15=   240÷4=

3 Without working it out, circle the sum in each pair which will give the higher answers.

| **a.** 1286 | **b.** 1286 | **a.** 92 | **b.** 92 | **a.** 40 | **b.** 60 |
| + 127 | + 137 | × 5 | × 6 | $\frac{40}{10}$ | $\frac{60}{10}$ |

| **a.** 124÷4 | **b.** 124÷6 | **a.** 358 | **b.** 358 | **a.** 151 | **b.** 151 |
| **a.** 72÷3 | **b.** 72÷6 | − 21 | − 17 | × 7 | × 6 |

4. Three of these answers are wrong. Can you say which three?
   a. 24__   **b.** 24__   **c.** 24__   **d.** 24__   **e.** 24__   **f.** 24__
   × 10   × 5   ×10   ×5   ×10   ×5
   2046   1204   2400   1235   5318   1240

5. Arrange the digits, three in each box, so that the difference between the numbers in the two boxes is as great as possible.

   1, 2, 3, 4, 5, 6.

ANSWERS

.3 Digital Dots: The mystery picture is a space rocket.

.4 A ½ is a ½ is a ½: Activity.

.5 Patterns with ten: Activity.

.6 What is it?: The mystery picture is a crab.

.7 Boxed in:

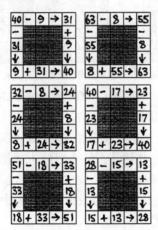

4	1	5
3	5	8
7+6		13

9	4	13
2	8	10
11	12	23

5	2	7
1	3	4
6	5	11

5	6	11
2	2	4
7	8	15

4	6	10
4	3	7
8	9	17

4	6	10
6	5	11
10	11	21

6	3	9
1	8	9
7	11	18

12	4	16
1	3	4
13	7	20

2	8	10
12	6	18
14	14	28

.8 Twenty up: Activity.

.9 They all add up to 20.

.10 Square dance:

40	−	9	→	31
−				+
31				9
↓				↓
9	+	31	→	40

63	−	8	→	55
−				+
55				8
↓				↓
8	+	55	→	63

32	−	8	→	24
−				+
24				8
↓				↓
8	+	24	→	32

40	−	17	→	23
−				+
23				17
↓				↓
17	+	23	→	40

51	−	18	→	33
−				+
33				18
↓				↓
18	+	33	→	51

28	−	15	→	13
−				+
13				15
↓				↓
15	+	13	→	28

.11 Nets: These are the six nets of a cube.

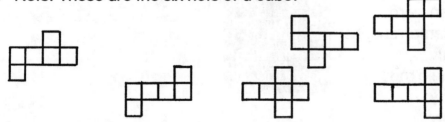

.12 Take it away:

(Bottom left hand column, top to bottom.) 15, 39, 27, 27, 17, 27, 4, 45, 37, 55.

(Bottom right hand column, top to bottom.) 23, 12, 24, 16, 36, 49, 11, 29, 41, 45.

.13 All for nought: Activity.

P.14 Number palindromes: 89 or 98 are the two-digit numbers that take the longest to produce a palindrome using this method.

P.15 Turnaround: Activity.

P.16 Ricky Robot: Ricky should be recognizable but he will have been distorted along the lines of the grid.

P.18 The Great Divide:
Numbers which will divide by 5: 40, 25, 935, 1980, 1235, 110, 365, 820, 400. Numbers that do not divide exactly by 5: 18, 16, 97, 44, 173, 219, 511, 802, 1321.
Rule: A number which divides by 5 will have 5 or 0 as the last digit.

P.19 Numbers that divide by 3: 12, 93, 105, 231, 540, 306, 117.
Numbers that do not divide exactly by 3: 20, 44, 65, 53, 79, 118.
Rule: A number which divides by 3 is a number the sum of whose digits when added up will divide by 3.
Rule for numbers dividing by 4: The last two digits will divide exactly by 4

P.20 Tens: Activity.

P.21 Activity.

P.22 Number cross:

P.23 Digital walls: The top brick of the small wall should contain the number 70. The top of the larger wall should contain the number 294. A quicker way of calculating the answer is to discover how many times each number is added in on its way to the top. For a wall with five bricks at its base, it is 1, 4, 6, 4, 1. Now the answer can be calculated by multiplying each of the numbers in the base line of bricks that number of times, and adding together the answers: $(3×1)+(1×4)+(7×6)+(4×4)+(5×1)=70$.

P.24 Add a ten: Activity.

P.26 Hidden words:

P.27 Concentric shapes: Activity.

P.28 Four in a row: Activity.

P.29 Activity.

P.30 An assortment: **1**. Digit = 0, d is correct. **2**. e.g. If $27×24 = 648$, then $27×12$ must equal half as much because 12 is half of 24. **3**. b, b, a, a, b, a, b. **4**. a, b, e. **5**. 654 and 123 produce a difference of 531.